MOVING ON...

Pathways to personal growth

to reach

by Margaret Pinkerton

the dawn

one must

move across

the path of

the night

ETERNITY INK

Moving On ...

Pathways to personal growth

Copyright © Brahma Kumaris Raja Yoga Centres Inc. 1996

Published by ETERNITY INK

78 Alt Street, Ashfield, NSW 2131 Australia

Printed October 1996 in Sydney, Australia on recycled paper.

Reprinted January1999, March 2000

Pinkerton, Margaret.

Moving on : pathways to personal growth.

ISBN 0 646 22254 6.

1. Meditation. 2. Spiritual healing. I. Title.

158.12

Edited by Jaie Watts & Peter Croucher

This book has been produced for the Brahma Kumaris World Spiritual University (BKWSU), a non-profit organisation, with the aim to share information as a community service for the spiritual growth of individuals. The Brahma Kumaris World Spiritual University exists to serve the family of humanity: to assist individuals to discover and experience their own spirituality and personal growth, to understand the significance and consequences of individual action and global interactions and to reconnect and strengthen their eternal relationship with the Supreme. The BKWSU is a non-governmental organisation with consultative status with the United Nations Economic and Social Council and UNICEF. Headed by women since its founding in 1936, the University now has more than 3,500 centres in 65 countries worldwide.

Contents

MOVING ON...

Pathways to personal growth

There is a difference between being alive and being able really to live and enjoy life. This book is about learning how to do the latter, through a process of self-transformation and meditation.

Although this book has been written specifically for people with a life-threatening illness, it is relevant for any person wishing to explore the process of self-transformation as an essential part of improving overall health and well-being.

It is increasingly being recognised that physical health is closely related to mental, emotional and spiritual states of being. When mental, emotional or spiritual experiences are negative and unbalanced, the effectiveness of the immune system is decreased, weakening the body's ability to fight physical disease.

Health practitioners can provide treatment for physical disease. However, it is each individual's responsibility to develop the awareness and process to rebalance mental, emotional and spiritual experiences towards positivity, health and well-being.

FOREWORD

In my own experiences of treating and caring for people affected by illnesses such as cancer, AIDS, motor neurone disease and multiple sclerosis, I have always been struck by the vast and unique differences individuals and families have in approaching their situation. Some are utterly shocked by the initial confrontation of ill-health and the prospect of facing change, dependency or death. Following, or even during, this initial reaction, many will simply accept medical advice about management of their condition. Much hope tends to be invested in such treatment even though outcomes may not, in reality, be as good as desired. There is usually uncertainty and anxiety, even if the implications of the diagnosis can be contained through the hope of successful medical management. Anger, guilt, depression and blaming oneself or others are common experiences particularly if there has been a delay, either in seeking medical advice or in the doctor's making of the diagnosis. Sorrow and grief are especially experienced by those who are considered incurable at diagnosis or who have experienced major changes in function and appearance. There is much emotional dependency then on support from others, either within the family, from groups or from individual counsellors. Thus the trauma experienced is physical, emotional and social. It is also spiritual, in the form of a confrontation with mortality, which is always experienced, whether the condition is curable or not.

While some people become primarily fearful and dependent as a consequence of their illness, others adopt a more positive attitude, seeking a deeper understanding of the nature and significance of their situation. This usually entails obtaining information about the disease itself and evaluating the available treatments. They also consider what they can do themselves, in terms of lifestyle changes or mental attitude, either to help themselves get well or to maintain quality of life. This often involves gathering and processing information about complementary therapies, diet and meditation. A positive attitude is developed towards self-help and enhanced personal control, with an approach to healing which is broader than mere dependence on physical treatments. Generally these unique individuals consider that a holistic approach to healing deals with the root psychological, emotional, environmental or spiritual causes of disease.

One pitfall I have observed in adopting complementary and attitudinal approaches to self-healing has been the emphasis on controlling the disease, such that this becomes a yardstick of success or failure. Thus, if the disease progresses, an emotional crisis of personal failure, guilt and despair emerges in some people who were previously so positive in their attitude. It usually occurs when the person has invested his or her energy entirely in the one outcome of cure. This shows us that the seed of what is often called a positive attitude might really be the fear of dying and raises the question of what is really meant by a positive attitude.

Healing may best be considered the attainment of spiritual well-being in which I experience inner peace, regardless of the physical condition. By switching the emphasis from disease control to personal enlightenment I can envisage healing as a state of self-realisation and renewal of spirituality. The illness might then be viewed as a stimulus for personal growth, a cleansing process for my inner life. In this way I can adopt an attitudinal approach, hopeful of remission, without dependence on this outcome to maintain peace of mind.

Moving On is an exceptional manual, highly recommended for people wishing to adopt this approach to healing. It provides a concise understanding of the nature of consciousness and outlines how to transform negative attitudes. Through self-respect one is encouraged to develop the qualities of forgiveness and unconditional love as part of letting go of the past. *Moving On* concludes with an enlightening look at acquiring true acceptance in the face of death and the development of spirituality as a way of life. The focus of meditation is developed throughout the book with every theme brought to life by written commentaries, which are beautifully captured in the *Moving On* cassette tapes, specially designed to accompany this book.

ROGER COLE, MB BS, FRACP – Specialist Physician in Cancer Medicine
Director of Palliative Care Services, Illawarra Area Health Service, NSW, Australia

Chapter 1 **ATTITUDES**

Choosing the way I want to live my life

All human beings will face death at some time. However, I may forget that I can and do choose the way I am experiencing life today. The way in which I experience events around me is dependent upon my perception of and attitude to those events. I may not be able to change or control my circumstances and environment, such as health and finances. However, I can control the way I perceive and deal with those circumstances.

My attitudes and my state of mind can be independent of the condition of the body and the world around me. Even though my body may not be well, it is still possible for me to be happy and peaceful. In the same way, it is possible to be physically well and yet be unhappy or peaceless.

The process that often happens is that I link my own happiness to external events. For instance: 'If only those people would behave the way I want them to behave, then I would be happy' or 'If only I had good health, then I'd be happy.' However, happiness is an internal state of being which cannot be found permanently in external things. These days more and more problems arise, owing to changing circumstances in the state of finances, health and relationships. The more that I try to control these circumstances to secure happiness, the more unhappy I become because I can't control them. When I try to attain stability and physical security, it often eludes me. Furthermore, when my sense of identity is linked to external objects and events, then any

HOW NEGATIVE THOUGHTS LEAD TO NEGATIVE OUTCOMES

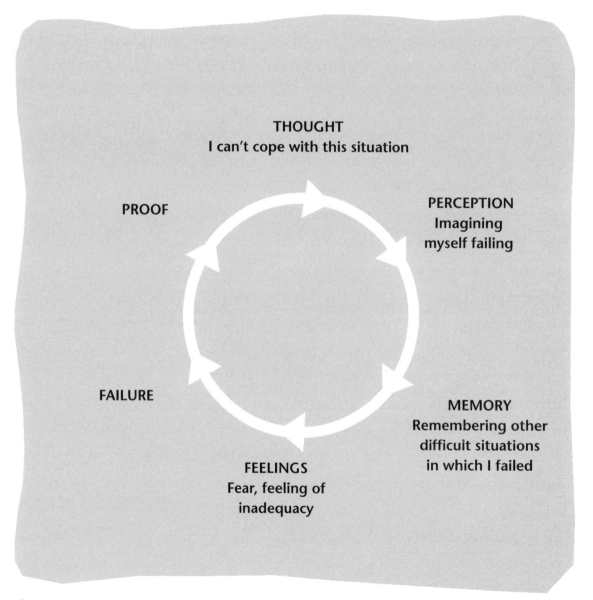

THOUGHT
I can't cope with this situation

PERCEPTION
Imagining
myself failing

PROOF

MEMORY
Remembering other
difficult situations
in which I failed

FAILURE

FEELINGS
Fear, feeling of
inadequacy

real fluctuation in these will lead to a feeling of failure. For instance: 'I am an OK person because my business is good' or 'I'm OK because my health is good.' Then if my business or health fails, 'I' feel worthless and a failure.

It is important :

- to experience and separate one's identity from external objects, events and circumstances;
- to understand, develop and practise positive attitudes in one's life.

The first aspect will be dealt with in chapter two. For now, let us address positive attitudes.

CYCLES OF THOUGHTS

My mental attitudes and reactions to circumstances around me can be either positive or negative, and the reactions that I experience usually become habitual. For instance, some people habitually worry when things go wrong, others get angry and so on.

I can change habitual reactions, but first I need to understand how the mind works. The mind thinks, feels, creates ideas, imagines and remembers. Thoughts arise because of external situations, other people and past influences, i.e. memories. Different circumstances and situations, people or events may trigger thought processes and memories that are happy or sad.

HOW POSITIVE THOUGHTS LEAD TO POSITIVE OUTCOMES

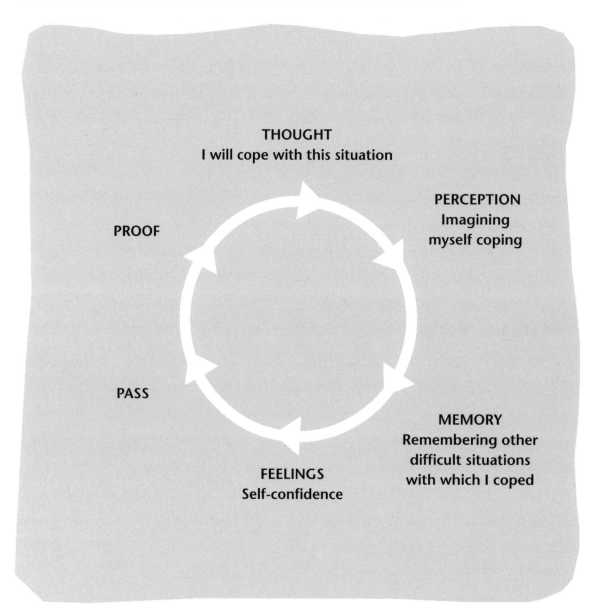

THOUGHT
I will cope with this situation

PERCEPTION
Imagining
myself coping

PROOF

MEMORY
Remembering other
difficult situations
with which I coped

PASS

FEELINGS
Self-confidence

Thought processes lead to inner experiences or emotions and these give rise to further identical or similar thoughts, evoking the same reactions. Negative cycles of thoughts and feelings lead to stress, feelings of loss of control, anxiety and worry. Situations may seem bigger or worse than they really are. Thinking becomes focused on the failures in life. Sustained negative attitudes over a period of time are often reflected in the body in the form of stress symptoms, muscle tension or the weakening of the immune system, which may cause or hasten the onset of physical illness. Positive thought cycles lead to feelings of inner confidence, being in control, calmness and clarity in making decisions for myself and others. I can keep situations in perspective. For example, I can understand that for every area of my life that has gone wrong there are many areas for which I can still be thankful.

Elisabeth Kübler-Ross in *To Live Until We Say Goodbye*[1] has noted that there are four quadrants comprising the human personality, namely the physical, spiritual, mental and emotional. People can be well if all these are functioning both individually and together in harmony. Experiencing positive thoughts and attitudes helps people to experience mental, emotional and spiritual health, which will ultimately be reflected in physical health.

[1] *To Live Until We Say Goodbye* E.Kübler-Ross, Prentice-Hall Inc. Englewood Cliffs NJ 1978

CHOOSING POSITIVE ATTITUDES

Meditation is the process by which it is possible to create new and positive thought patterns and to break the old, familiar and negative cycles of thinking. When I meditate, I am practising the art of choosing positive thoughts. With regular meditation, gradually concentration and the strength of the mind to choose positive thoughts increase and the effect flows over into my attitude to life.

Any person can change and develop positive habits of thinking. It is never too late to change. In time meditation goes further than thinking and becomes an experience. For example, I can tell myself that I am peaceful, but when I experience being peaceful, then I know I am. As my personal experiential meditation develops, so does my inner strength, my inner healing and my perception of my own positive qualities, such as peace, contentment, tranquillity or whatever I choose.

Meditation Commentary – **Orbs of Light**

I concentrate on my breathing. I begin to breathe more deeply, breathing in and out. I can feel and loosen up all the muscles in my body, from the top of my head to the toes of my feet, breathing deeply, in and out, loosening all the muscles in my body.

After some moments of breathing deeply, I focus my attention on the soles of my feet. I feel a soft vibration there. Slowly I bring my attention up through my ankles to my knees and then on up to my pelvis. I am now aware of the whole of my legs, just my legs. No other part of my body attracts my attention. I'm aware of my legs and I visualise my two legs covered with an all-white irradiant light. Only white light covers my legs from the soles of my feet up to my pelvis. I now create a strong thought that only health should reign within my legs. Only health should reign within my legs.

I take my awareness upward, through my pelvis until I reach my abdomen. I visualise in and around my navel and the small of my back a white-blue light, a white-blue irradiant light in the form of a nebula. I create a strong thought that full health should reign in my entire physical body. Full health should reign in my entire physical body.

I move my awareness upward, up to my chest, near my heart, and I visualise both inside and around my chest a white-rose light, a white-rose irradiant light in the form of a nebula. I create a strong thought that complete health will reign within my sentiments and emotions and that peace and tranquillity will prevail in my mind. Complete health will reign within my sentiments and emotions, and peace and tranquillity will prevail in my mind. Keeping the awareness of the white-blue light, covering the lower part of my body, and the white-rose light, covering the upper part of my body up to my neck, slowly I take my awareness down through my arms, down through my arms until I reach my palms and fingers. I visualise my arms and hands covered in an all-white irradiant light. I create a strong thought for complete health throughout my arms and hands — complete health throughout my arms and hands.

I take my awareness upward through my shoulders till I reach the centre of my head. I visualise a white-golden light, covering both the inside and outside of my head, a white-golden irradiant light, enveloping my head and extending about six inches beyond it in every direction. I create a strong thought for complete health within my inner being and to be able to use my thought in the right way — complete health within my inner being and the ability to use my thought in the right way.

And now, with my mind I see my whole body, the white-golden light enveloping and surrounding my head, the white-rose light in and around my chest and the white-blue light in and around my abdominal region.

Now I visualise a white light surrounding my entire body, my whole body within a white aura of light, a vibrating white luminosity. I am in the centre of this white luminous light. I make a strong thought that this white luminous light will protect me from anything that could bring me harm. The light will protect me from anything that could bring me harm.

I create three thoughts in my mind:

- *May peace reign inside my entire physical body.*
- *May harmony reign within my inner being.*
- *May absolute tranquillity prevail in my thoughts.*

I breathe deeply for a few more moments, and slowly bring my awareness back to my present surroundings.

(THIS COMMENTARY IS RECORDED WITH SPECIALLY COMPOSED MEDITATION MUSIC ON THE CASSETTE *MOVING ON 1.*)

Meditation Commentary – **The Forest**

After making myself very comfortable, I focus upon my own breath. I become aware that I'm breathing in and out. I notice the regularity of my breath in and out. With every breath out I let go of any tightness or stiffness within my body. With every breath out I can feel my whole body becoming loose and relaxed. As I breathe in, I imagine I'm breathing in a special energy of calmness and tranquillity. With every breath in I feel more calm and relaxed.

Now I imagine that I'm walking along a path towards a beautiful forest and, as I enter the forest, I look all around me and I notice the tall trees, the vines, the ferns on the forest floor and, amongst the greenery of the forest floor, hundreds of delicate flowers of many different colours. Up above I can see a blue sky and the rays of the sun, shining through the trees, illuminating the flowers and ferns on the forest floor, bathing them in an energy of bright light. The energy of the colours I observe in the forest, as well as the fresh air, is helping me to relax more and more as I walk along the forest path.

Ahead of me now I see a small river, winding its way deep into the forest. I stand on the bank of the river and I watch the water flowing away into the forest. Nearby me, very close, I notice a small boat. The boat is not tied down and seems about to drift away down the river. I decide to look deeply within myself and bring to my awareness any negative aspects about myself that I'd like to be free of — perhaps worry or fear, anxiety or self-doubt, anger or frustration. I create an image in my mind that represents these

14

negative aspects of myself, some image, whether abstract or literal, that, to me, represents my negative aspects, and into this image I encase my negative aspects. I notice again the shape and colour of this image.

Just before the boat by my feet drifts away, I place the image within the boat and I give the boat a gentle push. The boat is drifting away and I watch it, floating deep into the forest, floating, gliding away from me, into the forest, until it's out of sight. I feel so light and at ease, so free and relaxed.

Continuing on along the forest path, I become aware of the rays of the sun, shining on me, bathing me in a warm, bright light. The light surrounds my body like a white-golden mist. I feel so safe and protected. The warmth and light touch my heart. It's as if my heart opens up with feelings of warmth and love, both for myself as well as for others. I can recognise the good things about myself, my own special qualities, my own strengths, and I feel very comfortable about focusing on these and I send out this energy of loving acceptance, out into the forest and beyond, and it reaches the hearts of others. Surrounded by the warmth and light of the sun's rays, I'm aware of how I can create my thoughts and feelings and experience life in the way that I want.

Soon it will be time to leave the forest. The path is now leading me out of the forest. In my own time I bring my awareness back to my present surroundings and when I'm ready, I stretch and take in a deep breath.

(THIS COMMENTARY IS RECORDED WITH SPECIALLY COMPOSED MEDITATION MUSIC ON THE CASSETTE *MOVING ON 1*.)

Chapter 2 THE INNER SELF

Rediscovering the peace and love within my inner being

My inner self is the true 'I'. It is quite separate from what my body looks like, the state of my health, how much money I have or the roles I am playing at this time of my life. My inner self is my soul or spirit. It is non-physical and is a form of light and energy. My inner being manifests itself through my thoughts and feelings and emits vibrations that correspond to these thoughts and feelings. The inner self or soul also reflects outwardly and can be perceived and experienced through the eyes and face.

However, if I mistakenly define 'who I am' according to my job, my role, my health or by my physical attributes or capabilities, then I put myself in a position whereby perceived failures in these areas will lead to feelings of failure. For example: 'I have lost my job or my health and therefore I'm no good.' In Western culture the norms of competition and achievement can support this process because individuals often get used to comparing themselves with the external achievements and attributes of others and may find they don't measure up.

The way I think, whether positive or negative, is a true reflection of the condition or state of health of my inner being. If my thoughts are primarily negative, critical and judgemental of both myself and others, then my inner self will be unbalanced or in a state of emotional and mental ill-health, leading to experiences of bitterness, torment, confusion, stress and so on. I will then tend to perceive myself as not coping or as a failure and unable to be in control of my life.

Alternatively, if my thoughts are clear, calm, harmonious and positive, then I can experience within my inner being peace, contentment, love and so on. I then have a corresponding self-concept of confidence, self-acceptance and of being in control of my own life experience.

In fact, the natural state of being of the inner self is entirely positive. In nature a plant without blemish or disease appears very beautiful. So too, the inner self in its true and natural state is beautiful and blemish-free. The soul in its original pure state expresses its natural positive qualities such as peace, joy, love and serenity. Just as the physical body catches germs and becomes sick, in the same way the inner self catches the germs of negativity and becomes unhealthy.

Negative states of mind and negative experiences are not an intrinsic part of the inner being. They are forms of learnt behaviour, often activated as coping mechanisms to deal with stressful situations and change. They may also reflect the values and expectations of society at the time.

While it is not always possible to return the body to a perfect state of health, mental and emotional negativity and anguish can be 'cured' by positive thinking and meditation. The health of the inner being can be totally restored, bringing the soul back to experiences of contentment, peace and happiness. The first step in working towards the mental, emotional and spiritual health of the inner being or soul is to understand how thinking or consciousness operates.

The faculties of consciousness are the mind, intellect and subconscious

Mind The mind consists of the conscious thoughts of which the individual is aware. Generally, before the practice of meditation, the mind jumps rapidly from one thought to another. The conscious thoughts may be either positive or negative. Either way, these thoughts will lead to the corresponding emotions. For example, I first begin to 'think' angry thoughts and then I 'feel' angry. Sustained negative thinking over a long period of time can be wasteful, repetitive and drain individuals of their physical, mental and emotional energy. A healthy mind will have positive thoughts.

Intellect The intellect is the part of the consciousness that assesses the conscious thoughts of the mind. For example, if I am having angry thoughts about something, my intellect may say something like, 'Don't be angry with that person - it's not his fault.' However, if my intellect is weak, it cannot control the mind and therefore my angry thoughts and emotions will not stop. A strong intellect will be able to control the mind and emotions and then I can change my thinking as I wish. The intellect may also be clear or unclear in its perception. For example, my intellect may tell me I am justified in blaming someone else for my troubles and therefore it's OK to become angry. However, possibly my perception is wrong and I am not justified in blaming others. The intellect is also responsible for deciding whether or not I will bring my thoughts into action. A weak intellect may say 'no', for example, to bringing angry thoughts into action but then may not be able to prevent this from happening. With a strong intellect I will never lose control and do things I may regret later. A healthy intellect has strength, clarity and good judgement.

Subconscious Thinking and behaviour tend to move into patterns and become habits or tendencies in the personality. These habits, tendencies or personality traits then sit in the subconscious, ready to be triggered into thoughts by external circumstances and events. For example, if I have always reacted to bad news with worry, upset and stress, and now I hear I have health problems or a member of my family has health problems, then I very quickly react in the same way. This pattern of reaction has become habitual. My subconscious holds a store of all my positive and negative qualities. For example, all individuals have the quality of peace, because they can remember sometime, somewhere in their lives when they experienced this. But perhaps I haven't used this quality regularly for a long time and so have got more used to pulling out of my subconscious the negative qualities of fear, anger and worry. In a healthy subconscious positive qualities are dominant and are easily transferred to the mind as positive thoughts, even when external events are going 'wrong'.

THE FACULTIES OF CONSCIOUSNESS

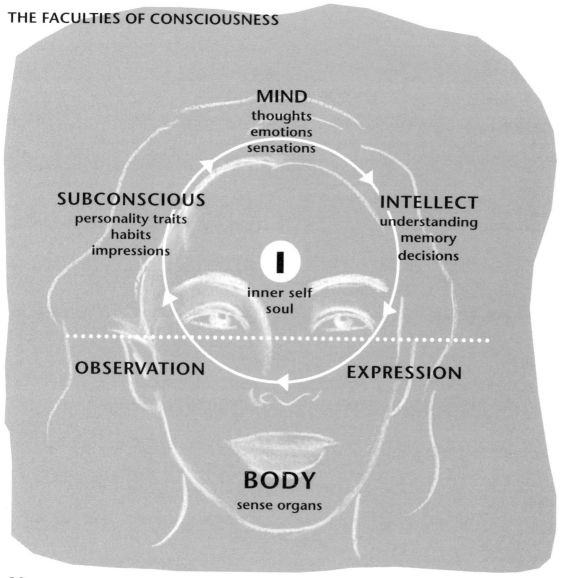

MIND
thoughts
emotions
sensations

SUBCONSCIOUS
personality traits
habits
impressions

INTELLECT
understanding
memory
decisions

I
inner self
soul

OBSERVATION

EXPRESSION

BODY
sense organs

Meditation will help me to experience and strengthen the positive qualities in my subconscious, control and guide the thoughts of the mind into positivity and strengthen the intellect so that it has more clarity and control. At first I may find it easier to control and change negativity in my actions rather than negativity in my thinking and experience. However, as I stop bringing negative thoughts and subconscious habits into action, they begin to weaken.

The process whereby I begin to break the negative cycle of experience within the inner self will start through positive meditation experiences and by paying attention to the quality of my actions. Then I will be coming closer to the truth of the self which is the experience of positivity, harmony, peace and contentment.

Positivity is like a muscle − it will atrophy with disuse and strengthen when used. The more I experience my positive qualities, the more I naturally use them in my actions and so they become stronger. As this process continues, I begin to feel more security, strength, joy, stability, with no fear of loss. I am becoming internally healthy.

As I strengthen my own internal positive thoughts and experiences, I become free from the influence of external circumstances such as 'I can't be sure I'll ever be healthy again; that's why I'm always unhappy.' As I start to rely more on my own inner resources, strengths and positivity, I find fluctuations in external events will no longer mean fluctuations in my experience of peace and happiness or in my own sense of identity. When I achieve this, then I can feel the freedom of being able to experience peace and happiness when I want and not just when things are going right. As I develop this ability, my feelings of self-worth, self-confidence and self-respect grow.

When I develop faith in myself and choose not to react negatively to external circumstances, then I can actually become the influencer of external situations. For example, if I remain calm with others who are angry or upset with me, then they are more likely to calm down sooner.

It is useful to remember that individuals communicate through their vibrations as well as their words. Communication through vibrations can be acutely important when the state of health of individuals does not allow them to communicate through words. That is, they can 'feel' when others are calm and accepting and this soothes them.

Meditation Commentary – **Balloon**

Focusing my thoughts on my own inner being, I begin to think about who I am. I move my thoughts away from my name, my role, my possessions and my health, all the temporary things which earth me. I am seeking to experience the 'I' that owns all these. Who am 'I'?

I feel myself as living energy. I am a concentrated spark of life-energy and I am radiating light. I let all the pettiness and problems drift away and I allow myself to feel very light, free from all burdens and worries. I remember a time previously in my life when I felt like this, perhaps as a child, or on holiday, no fear, no heaviness, just me, feeling easy and light, glad to be alive.

Now, in my mind's eye I see a field ahead of me and in this field I see a huge beautiful helium-filled balloon, attached to a basket. The balloon is shimmering in the sunlight with a deep blue-green colour. I step into the basket of the balloon and seat myself very comfortably and the balloon is launched. As my balloon lifts higher and higher, any remaining heaviness and burden drop from my mind and the light-energy that is me begins to shine and sparkle like a star. Even my body begins to feel light and weightless.

My balloon drifts past sun-drenched open fields of green, high above, floating, drifting. I'm floating now over a crystal-blue lake, surrounded by gentle rolling hills. From the lake rises a refreshing breeze. I feel it on my face, on my cheeks, playing with my hair. As I drift further and further across the lake, I feel very inspired by the beauty and peace that are all around me.

I notice that the peacefulness of the scene that I am watching is now becoming a part of me. I feel peaceful. I am peaceful. I don't need to go anywhere to find peace. It's part of my own identity, my own original nature.

I concentrate my thoughts fully and I experience the quality of peace, washing over me and pervading my whole being. My own inner peace enters every corner of my consciousness and I feel calm, serene, silent and light, at peace with myself. I know this is truly 'me'. This quality of peace comes from deep within me. I've released the lock on my mind and now I am able to experience silence, lightness and peace throughout my whole being.

As my natural state of peace emerges, I discover my own strength, my own inner power. I am a being of light, silent and powerful, radiating light and peace. High in my balloon I notice that, when I feel this way, the entire world looks colourful, beautiful, a wonderful place in which to be.

I'm aware that I am experiencing loving feelings about myself and I send these loving feelings onto the earth and all its living beings. My peaceful vibrations of love and light are reaching out and touching other living beings, and nature, helping them to experience the touch of peace, the touch of peace.

It's time for my balloon to descend slowly to the ground, gently descending, gently. Although this journey is finishing, I will bring back with me the imperishable experience of who I really am, a being of peace, love and light, with unlimited strength. I can keep this with me always because it is mine and no person or situation can take it away. And my basket touches ground. Gently I return to the consciousness of the room in which I am sitting.

(THIS COMMENTARY IS RECORDED WITH SPECIALLY COMPOSED MEDITATION MUSIC ON THE CASSETTE *MOVING ON 1*.)

Meditation Commentary – **Inner Self**

For the next few moments I'm going to reflect on my own inner being, upon who I really am. In the past I've often thought of myself by the name which I am called, or by what my body looks like, including the condition of my health, or perhaps the job I've been doing or the role I've played. I now understand these roles, names and appearances are connected with my body, with the part that I play in this life. I'm now going to allow myself to feel the life within my body.

I am living energy, emanating from an infinitesimal point, radiating out in the form of light and vibrations. I am a star, radiating energy and light. This is my inner being, my soul. This is me.

This energy is giving life to my body. My body is my vehicle and I, the soul, am the life within this body. I can make the body move. I can keep the body at rest. I, the soul, exist and I can think and feel.

Sometimes I feel pain and hurt, and sometimes I feel tranquillity and peace. Now

I understand that the pain and hurt I have felt have come to me through the body, and my qualities of tranquillity and peace are the true nature of my soul. I focus on my soul alone. My awareness of my body fades.

I begin to feel light, travelling beyond the awareness of my body into the consciousness of being a soul. Deep reserves of peace and calm emerge from within me. Deep within myself I feel my own original pure energy of peace. I'm surrounded by a feeling of peace, immersed in a deep experience of peace.

I am beyond hurt, beyond pain, beyond the body. I exist. I have awareness. My consciousness is light and free. My life extends beyond my body. Even without a body, I, the living energy, will continue. I am eternal. I am a being of light, the embodiment of peace. I'm free, bodiless, travelling beyond the awareness of my body into an experience of light and peace. My awareness is beyond fear, beyond hurt and pain. I'm always safe because I can never lose myself. I am for always. I exist forever, and I'm so peaceful, content just to be who I am and for these few moments free of the limitations of this physical world.

Experiencing the original, pure state of my inner being in this way accesses new feelings within me about myself. I can trust myself, accept myself, love myself. I am me and I'm living my life, my role, through this body to the best of my ability and that is enough.

Having love for myself enables me to be gentle on myself. I don't have to punish myself for doing or being what I'm not or what I can't become. The limitations I experience in my health, my roles or in doing what I want to do are simply restrictions in acting through my body and my soul is vast and unlimited. Within my soul I can experience the limitless wealth of my treasures of peace, love, joy, serenity, and I share this with others. I do this now. I share my own pure energy of peace and love with those who are close to me, either physically close or those who may be far away and whom I can bring close in my mind. As I love and accept myself and others, my soul regains the feeling of its own harmony and fullness. My inner spirit is rebalancing. Experiencing the life of my soul beyond my body has allowed my inner strength of harmony, balance, purity and peace to emerge once again. I have the strength to love and be peaceful and I have the freedom just to be me. And in my own time, when I feel ready, I allow my thoughts to return to the room in which I'm sitting, but only when I'm ready.

(THIS COMMENTARY IS RECORDED WITH SPECIALLY COMPOSED MEDITATION MUSIC ON THE CASSETTE *MOVING ON 1.*)

Chapter 3 SELF-ESTEEM
Learning to believe in myself

Individuals all carry an awareness or image of themselves within their minds. In a general sense each individual has two choices: to doubt the self and have feelings of lack of worth; or to believe in the self and have self-regard. Both of these possibilities may be experienced at different times.

Throughout life most individuals have added some layers of doubt to their self-concept, either because of mistakes made in the past, real or imagined, or because they have accepted the negative attitudes, opinions or actions other people have towards them.

One of the most essential parts of the process of self-transformation is to remove these layers of doubts and replace them with feelings of self-value, self-respect, self-love and self-acceptance.

The real nature of every soul is love. If one is not able to love, either the self or others, then somewhere there has been an injury to the soul. The meditation process develops the ability to have a positive attitude towards oneself. Through meditation I learn the process of accepting and experiencing my own qualities, virtues, values and specialties. For example, in meditation when I accept and experience the thought, 'I am a peaceful, loving and lovable being', I am cleansing myself of inferiority complexes or the negative opinions and feelings of others.

The greatest gift I can give to myself is to believe in myself. If I continually say to myself, 'I haven't got the strength to cope' or 'I'm not good enough', then I won't be able to cope or I won't be good enough. When I lack faith in myself, I place restrictions on my own abilities to deal with challenges and change in my life. With self-respect I can face all situations. With lack of self-respect I get scared.

Each person is unique and individual. All individuals must maintain faith in their own specialties, even if others don't. Sooner or later when others start to feel some benefit from their specialties, they will be able to appreciate them.

I must accept and value the specialties I have and not think about what I can't do or that my specialties are not good enough. Nevertheless, all individuals have weaknesses in some areas. I must accept this as a totality of the self and understand I am working to transform my negative attributes anyway.

Without self-esteem and feelings of self-worth, when something goes wrong in my life – for example, my health breaks down – I allow this to be proof that 'I am not OK'. I have to learn to let go of measuring the quality of my identity according to the state of my health, my achievements, my roles or my body image. If I don't, then there will always be some discontentment and unhappiness within me.

If I don't have true and real feelings of self-regard and self-love, I usually feel an inner emptiness which I compensate for with ego. Ego arises from lack of: self-respect. It is a false pride, a false belief about the self. Ego makes individuals feel either that they are better than others or not good enough. Ego drives them to 'prove' their worth through external 'show' or achievements and often makes them jealous when others achieve and receive regard. With ego people put themselves down for making mistakes and tend to focus more on their own weaknesses and shortcomings.

Ego is a major cause of suffering. When the outer shell of ego is threatened, either by my own lack of achievement or by the opinion of others, then I get drained and hurt inside. I may respond with sensitivity, hurt or anger. For the well-being of the inner self it is essential that I break down the artificial prop of ego and develop a true sense of self-respect.

With self-respect I believe in myself. To believe in myself means to experience that 'whoever I am, whatever I am, I am OK' and that 'I can and will achieve whatever I need to achieve'. Self-worth, self-acceptance and self-confidence are positive self-affirmations. No matter what others are like, I am fine as I am. My motive for doing anything should not be to reach false and unrealistic expectations placed upon me by myself or others, but should come from a genuine sense of self-worth, self-reliance and an attitude of respect for myself and the task at hand. This is true confidence. I have ability, I am capable and, whatever I achieve, the outcome of that will be positive also. Moreover, I do not have to prove myself to anyone because I already know I am OK.

Meditation is a valuable tool to help me build up my self-esteem because meditation guides me to experience myself and my highest qualities independently from my successes or failures. I am then able to experience the unique virtues, specialties and qualities of my own inner spirit.

Having faith in myself increases my inner strength and flexibility to adapt to the changing circumstances in my life. When I don't believe in myself, then I don't have the confidence to accept and believe that I can cope with change. Then I may try and cling to the past, either by wishing things to be the way they were before or by resentfully remembering life's lost opportunities and how the present loss is yet another example of such lost opportunities.

When I have confidence and faith in myself, I do not perceive loss or change to be such a fearful thing. This is because I begin intuitively to feel that when something goes wrong in my life, it doesn't mean that I am not an intact, valuable and worthwhile human being. With this perception I don't feel a loss of control or as if my whole world is falling apart. I need to accept all of myself, including my weaknesses and my health problems. These are parts of me too and when I accept this, I can stop fighting a losing battle and move on.

When I believe in myself, I automatically develop faith in my abilities to rise above my fears, shame, guilt and other negative emotions. I can perceive the changing circumstances of life, even if traumatic, to be growth experiences, something from which I can emerge as a freer, more creative human being.

Then I become like a boat that is in the calm waters of the eye of a cyclone. The storms of life may be going on, but I have found the seat of inner stability with which to ride the storms. Like the boat, I am safe and protected. The lesson here is that, like the boat, I have to ride the storm and flow with it. If I attempt to jump into the storm and to fight it, I only get battered. I need to ride the storm of life and flow with life's destiny.

It helps if I can believe that the drama of life is evenly balanced between positive and negative forces and that ultimately the balance of stillness, calm, peace, serenity, happiness and joy will return to my life.

I can exaggerate worry and fear in my mind as much as I like or I can believe that ultimately things will work out for the best, even if the method for working things out is not what I wanted or planned. Again, I have the choice. Once I develop faith in myself and in life itself, it becomes easier to renounce my fear of what the future holds for me. This leaves me free to experience a sense of calmness and inner tranquillity in the here and now.

Meditation Commentary – **Self-esteem**

I turn my thoughts inwards, focusing on my own inner being. I allow the world with all its complexities, roles and relationships to slip away from my mind by filling my consciousness with thoughts of my own inner self: I am peaceful, I am light, I am energy – and from deep within myself I begin to radiate strength and acceptance.

I am standing on the shore of my life and with my inner eye I look upon the vast ocean of my inner being. Behind me I have left all the heaviness and burden of my worldly life. In front of me lie unlimited possibilities of new experiences.

My consciousness begins to open up to the vast, unlimited energy of the universe and beyond. In my mind's eye I see a star, a wondrous, radiant star of light that is emanating waves of peace, waves of love, towards me. I allow these waves to enter the depths of my inner self and I am immersed in waves of peace and love. It's as if I've become the form of peace itself, gentle light waves of peace, filling up my entire being. A divine energy of love is caressing me and the empty spaces within myself are being filled with love and light.

The universal divine energy and my own energy of light and peace combine as if one. I feel myself becoming whole again. The wounds and emptiness within my inner being are healing. I'm filling up with peace and love and acceptance for myself. My inner self is shining brightly with a light that no circumstance of life can dim. I am flowing with my destiny. I am a master, choosing how I will experience my destiny. I have the deepest faith in myself to guide myself through all the troubled waters of life. I understand how each troubled area within my life is leading to new depth and growth within my inner being. I believe in myself. I am whole, intact, full in the richness of my own strength and peace.

I am light enough to fly over the biggest mountain of obstacles that life can place in front of me. I have no need to exaggerate future possibilities and I can leave the past where it belongs, in the past.

I can feel the light and strength of my inner being, radiating out through my face and eyes like light waves of energy, peace and joy. I am experiencing the beginning of a journey of discovery into the vast treasures of experience that lie within the silence of myself.

Slowly, I begin to move my thoughts away from my inner, silent being and again I waken my consciousness to the world around me, the room in which I'm sitting. Slowly, slowly, I look around me, with my eyes. The peace and strength that have come to me from my inner journey are still reflecting out through my face, through my eyes. In time I know I will be able to keep this peace and strength with me all the time, always.

(THIS COMMENTARY IS RECORDED WITH SPECIALLY COMPOSED MEDITATION MUSIC ON THE CASSETTE *MOVING ON 1.*)

Chapter 4 RELATIONSHIPS

Expressing my inner self in interaction with others

When a member of the family becomes sick with a life-threatening illness, the relationships in a family may intensify and result in unresolved issues, conflicts, tensions or poor communication. Alternatively, it is a time when the family relationships can grow in their expression of honesty, acceptance, caring, sharing and communication.

Faced with the fact that the time together may be limited, if individuals can resolve and accept their differences, their hurtful memories, their unfulfilled expectations and move towards an honest expression of caring, sharing and effective communication, then they will have given to each other a timeless and wonderful gift. Long after the memory of the physical body fades, the memories of the relationship will remain.

First I need to understand the nature of relationships in a general way. The give and take of love, warmth and caring within relationships are a natural and intrinsic part of life. When I feel happy, at ease and content within my relationships, then I can feel peaceful and content within myself, and my relationships often reflect this. My relationships are a reflection of my attitudes and internal experiences, my strengths and weaknesses and my internal image of myself. Much of my life has probably been spent trying to feel secure and loved in my relationships with parents, friends, relatives, spouse and children. Sometimes my desire to feel security and love within my relationships is fulfiled and at other times it is not. When my relationships do not give me the experience of security and love, then I have a choice: either to blame others or to look at my own contribution to the situation. Even if I choose the first and blame others, they still may not change and the more I try to make them change, the more they may resent me and the more frustrated I may become. If I can have the wisdom and strength to look at my own contribution to my relationships, I can come to the realisation that the one thing I can change is myself and, moreover, when I change my own input into a relationship, then the relationship will often begin to resolve the conflicts and tensions or whatever the problems may be.

When reflecting on my own contribution to my relationships, it may be helpful to look at the following:

1. It is possible that when I can't accept others 'as they are' it is because I don't accept myself 'as I am'.

Through meditation and internal growth, as I begin to develop faith in myself and my abilities, without unrealistic comparisons with others, then I find my vision of others also becomes less critical. As acceptance of myself grows, I begin to accept others with all their strengths and weaknesses.

My relationships will improve when my own efforts to see myself with a positive vision are extended to seeing others with a positive vision. I need to make a conscious effort to focus on the strengths and good qualities of others and to accept their shortcomings.

By understanding myself as a soul and seeing others with the same vision I am more inclined to see the beauty and specialties of others, rather than judging them on their roles or achievements.

When others feel accepted, they will feel more at ease within the relationship and most likely I will find they will be more accepting of me. Having the strength to change my attitudes towards others can change the nature of my relationships.

2. Understand that 'true' love is unconditional.

If I love others only when they do or behave as I think they should, then I can never experience the depths of true, unfluctuating love. If I seek the love of others to fill up my own 'emptiness', I will never be satisfied because others are not perfect and therefore they cannot always give me what I want.

Furthermore, needing another's love and regard to fill up my own 'emptiness' means I have become dependent upon that person for my happiness. With this dependency I often become interested in others only as people to nourish my need and, when they don't or can't do this, I tend to define this as weakness, saying 'They are so selfish!' With such a vision I easily move away from appreciating the beauty of others.

Ultimately, close relationships can only work in the long term when both parties take responsibility to develop towards being complete in themselves. Then they can love and appreciate each other the way they are.

The expression of true love is one of giving. To love is to give of oneself. If I give love and caring in my relationships, regardless of what I receive in return, I come to understand that giving and caring for others is the true means of self-fulfilment. Through giving, I myself become full.

3. Love becomes a bondage when I bind others to my expectations.

This means I get hurt, angry or upset when others can't be the kinds of people I expected them to be, or they don't do things the way I expected them to. Such expectations of others develop from a concept of love that includes elements of ownership or possession. 'I love you, but I expect and need you to behave in a certain way that is of benefit to me and for my own peace of mind.' Ultimately, by letting go of my expectations of others, I become free from hurt, anger and frustration towards them.

People with life-threatening illnesses may feel frustrated or angry about losing control of their lives or about losing their hopes for the future. This anger is often a passing phase in coming to terms with their own situation. However, the anger may be vented upon the person they love and trust the most.

If at this time I have the strength not to take this anger personally but to remain giving, accepting and loving, then it is more likely that the angry phase will pass more quickly without lasting damage or impression. This is saying to others: 'I know you are going through hell, but I accept you and I accept your struggle.' As the anger subsides, it can become possible to communicate about the 'real' issues behind the anger, for example, fear, worry, hurt.

Alternatively, carers, when faced with the possible loss of a loved one, can often feel resentment and anger because they are going to be left alone and they didn't expect this to happen. Their feelings may be amplified by other previous unfulfilled expectations within the relationship.

Even if an attempt is made to hide these feelings, it is most likely that the person who is the focus of this resentment will pick it up from facial expressions and other non-verbal communications. They, in turn, can often experience worry about how the spouse, parent, relative, friend or child will cope.

It is important to acknowledge feelings of resentment, anger and frustration and to realise they are normal, and to communicate these feelings in a loving and honest way — and not to feel guilty. Then a resolution is more likely to be found and, by communicating and sharing feelings, unknown strengths and solutions may emerge.

4. Sometimes it is difficult within a relationship to communicate caring, love and concern effectively.

When a partner within a relationship has a life-threatening illness, there are two choices: firstly, to live in a world of make-believe, pretend the situation is not there and to hide one's feelings or secondly, to begin to share the reality of the situation along with one's fears, worries and concerns.

Those who choose the second alternative soon realise that bringing up these issues is only hard at first and that it will ultimately bring a sense of relief and honesty into the relationship. They realise that caring isn't trying to protect others from the reality of the situation but that it is being able to listen, share concerns and offer support and acceptance. Many times the avoidance of this process is linked to one's own fears and inability to face the situation.

People choose their own time when they are ready to talk about the issues they are concerned about. One needs to pick up the signals that others are ready to communicate and express themselves. Often all that is needed is simply to listen and perhaps reflect to others what they are saying in order to clarify it. Listen carefully to decide whether they are asking for advice or simply wanting to talk.

Overall, attempts to share, care and give within relationships will be enhanced by one's own internal strengths, positive attitudes and methods of self-sustenance.

Meditation is a technique to support and sustain the self through positive thinking and the internal experiences of joy and peace. Meditation can be like taking a holiday within the self because, when I meditate, I take a rest from all my fears, worries and tensions.

It must be remembered, however, that it takes time and patience to move thoughts away from worries and fears, even temporarily. However, ultimately I have the choice to do this and my determination will bring it about. Eventually my meditation experiences will find expression in my daily life, attitudes and relationships. This can help those with whom I have close relationships to develop their own strength, peace and acceptance. The expression of these qualities will then become part of the relationship itself.

Meditation Commentary – **Acceptance**

I have become aware of my thoughts. I begin to relax my mind, slow down my thinking. I allow thoughts of peace to enter my consciousness. Deep within myself I have the quality of peace. I am peaceful and now I'm going to connect with the experience of this quality.

I feel the energy of peace coming into my consciousness. Vibrations of peace begin to emanate from within me. I can feel a small ball of peace like a pearl, deep within my inner being. As I focus on my inner ball of peace, my secret pearl, I experience it and it begins to grow. I feel waves of peace, vibrating throughout my whole body, and now my ball of peace bursts into a fountain of light and peace, showering drops of peace throughout my whole being.

Now my mind becomes still, silent, peaceful. My thoughts are held in an experience of peace. I am calm, content. I feel deep acceptance and serenity within myself. I am light. Light waves of peace are emanating from deep within me and I'm so free, so light, as though floating in a sea of peace.

I see a pathway of light, opening up in front of me. At the end of that pathway, I know, is the home of peace. The home of peace is drawing me upwards and silently, instantly, my thoughts travel to that vast, infinite oceanic peace, my home. I immerse my soul in this silent space. I feel a very strong and lovely presence, the presence of a great being of light who's gently showering waves of peace and love on me. I accept these vibrations of peace and love and they become part of me. The gift of peace, as vast as an ocean, is within me. I feel the company and nurturing of this most powerful, loving being. Now my experience of peace has become powerful. The vibrations of peace and love are reaching the deepest corners of my consciousness and they are healing me. I feel whole, I feel loved, I feel accepted. It's OK to be me. I like being me. My heart is full, full of light, love and peace, firstly for myself, and then I offer this as a donation to others in the form of my thoughts. I send peaceful feelings and good wishes to all those who are close in my heart. I see these people in front of me and send them my vibrations of deep peace and acceptance. I feel the happiness of giving and of allowing others just to be who they are. Feelings of honesty, closeness and caring are communicated between us all.

As I feel peaceful and accepting towards others, I understand that others can become peaceful and accepting towards me. I'm experiencing the true nature of love, no questions, no demands, no expectations, only giving and sharing of warmth, caring and acceptance.

I have such a resource of love and caring within me that my vibrations of peace and loving acceptance travel beyond my family and friends and reach others in the world who are also searching for peace and relief from suffering. As I send out these vibrations, my own reservoir of peace and caring becomes even deeper, strong enough to travel to any destination I choose.

I draw my thoughts back to the experience of myself. I've travelled the vast, unlimited spaces within myself and I've found that I am strong, peaceful and internally healthy. As I come back to the awareness of the room I am in, I bring with me feelings of calmness, silence, peace and well-being. As I continue to experience these qualities, they will automatically arise in my thoughts, words, actions and relationships with others. I can give others a timeless and imperishable gift, that of myself.

(THIS COMMENTARY IS RECORDED WITH SPECIALLY COMPOSED MEDITATION MUSIC ON THE CASSETTE *MOVING ON 1.*)

Chapter 5 LETTING GO
From sorrow moving towards acceptance and peace

The discovery that a family member or I have a life-threatening illness creates a crisis in our lives. However, if handled sensitively with caring, understanding and knowledge, all can emerge from the process stronger, wiser and more peaceful.

My experience in facing death is a product of my needs, my past grief experiences, my relationships, my spirituality, my life experiences and my future projections. However, the threat of dying does not have to be a nightmare unless I make one out of it. On the contrary, it can be a time when my inner wisdom, courage, strength and creativity emerge.

In *To Live Until We Say Goodbye,* Elisabeth Kübler-Ross states that her life's work is 'to help patients view a terminal illness not as a destructive, negative force, but as one of the wind storms in life that will enhance their inner growth and help them to emerge as a butterfly emerges from a cocoon, with beauty and a sense of peace and freedom.'

My reaction to dying and my grief are parts of a process with many phases and stages. However, whatever I am experiencing is always my choice. I can put my head in the sand and try and forget it. I can drown myself in self-pity or in anger and anguish, often displacing it onto others. I can face the future with fear and bargain with God for more time. Or I can say 'yes' to my illness, my pain, my emotions, my turmoil and the reaction of others and use these as an opportunity for inner growth, leading to increasing acceptance, peace and wisdom.

Whatever the choice, it is best if those around me try to understand and accept my needs. Reality cannot be forced and I will work through my own issues in my own time according to my own needs. However, I will be unable to choose the option of acceptance of my condition, along with the inner change and growth, if I remain stuck in my fears, frustrations, guilts, or if I am dwelling on past hurts, lost opportunities or unfulfilled expectations. One thing I need to do is to forgive, if not forget, thereby letting go and moving on. I need to forgive both myself and others.

I must forgive myself for all my past mistakes, lost opportunities and even my current illness. As I forgive myself, I can begin the process of letting go of dwelling in the past, of my frustrations about the present and of my fears for the future. When I forgive myself, I am beginning the process of letting go of my negative self-images which may be related to my roles, physical condition or personality. A negative self-image may lead me to think: 'I look different now I am sick; so people will think badly about me' or 'I can't work because I am sick and so I feel guilty and a failure' or 'My future is uncertain and therefore I feel fear.' When I approach others with these thoughts, I often prevent myself from feeling the love and acceptance they are giving me.

If I find it difficult to let go of my negative self-images, it may be because I have become attached to them and therefore find it hard to contemplate approaching life with different attitudes. I mistakenly perceive my weaknesses to be my strengths because I rely on them or because they have become habits. However, if I have the courage to let go of the weaknesses in my attitudes, the gap that is left inside myself can eventually become filled with positive attitudes.

Meditation facilitates this process by teaching how to concentrate on and develop strengths, positive qualities and self-esteem. As I practise this, I automatically begin to let go of my wasteful and negative thoughts and emotions.

As I develop the strength to forgive myself, I must also begin to forgive others for all the hurt and pain I may feel they have inflicted upon me. For this I have to let go of my anger and expectations that others 'should' have been more caring and loving or they 'should' have known how to give respect and meet my needs. As I forgive and let go, a sense of acceptance of others can develop, along with a feeling of acknowledgement that others have only done the best they could do at the time.

It is beneficial if I can personally communicate, in a caring way, my unfinished issues with others. However, if this is not possible, I can use meditation and visualisation to begin to resolve the issues.

When I am ready to let go and forgive, the meditation commentary, *Forgiveness*, at the end of this chapter may be useful.

Of course the process of forgiving another will not happen overnight. Feelings of hurt and anger must never be suppressed but acknowledged, worked through, and ultimately let go of when I am ready. Some people may need to express their fears, frustrations and guilt, to share their pain and agony or even to scream and rage. Whichever way I choose, the only important thing is that I am moving through the issues and am not hopelessly stuck in fear, hurt or anger.

This process of letting go can help me move towards an appreciation of what I have achieved in life, my happy moments and the precious shared times I have had, and still can have, with my loved ones. As fear, resentment and anger lose their grip on me, I can begin to 'live' again, each and every day.

Meditation assists in the process of 'letting go' by enabling me to get in touch with my own strengths and possibilities. As I learn to experience the inner self and my qualities as independent from my body, health and relationships, I come to touch the source of my inner strength and ability to resolve and accept change.

As I come to understand I am a worthwhile person, no matter what the state of my body or my other circumstances, I begin to develop faith in the ultimate outcome of life itself. As I often chose to experience negative attitudes in my life, now I can choose to let them go.

Letting go of unfinished business can be easier if I properly use the support systems around me. These may be friends, family, meditation, values or beliefs, religion and memories. Each has to be identified, explored and used by each person according to need.

Family reactions will contribute a lot to the response to illness. When family members can work through their own anger, resentment and guilt (for example, feeling they didn't do enough to stop the patient getting sick), then they can go through their own phase of grief and acceptance. There may come a time when family and friends have consciously to let go of their relationship with their dying loved one. If the family clings to the idea of the continuation of the relationship and that life will be unbearable without their loved one, and if they communicate to the dying person that they won't cope after the death, then it is much harder to live and die with peace and acceptance.

It is important that family members do not begin to cut themselves off from the outside world in order to attend to their sick relative. Family members need to continue to live their own lives without

All need to come to an acceptance that life is a process of change.

Individual growth lies in adaptation to change, in using the supports available and in perceiving every experience as an opportunity for growth and wisdom.

As we all live and let be, life has and will hold in store for us all a wealth of new experiences.

50

feeling guilty, and to recharge their batteries with whatever resources are available to them. When family members continue to live their own lives in whatever way they can, the adjustment to changing roles brought about by illness can be facilitated. All need to come to an acceptance that life is a process of change. Individual growth lies in adaptation to change, in using the supports available and in perceiving every experience as an opportunity for growth and wisdom. As we all live and let be, life has and will hold in store for us all a wealth of new experiences.

Meditation Commentary – **Forgiveness**

I close my eyes and sit comfortably and relax by taking a number of deep breaths. I remember and visualise one of my favourite beaches. In my imagination I see myself walking onto the beach, taking off my shoes and walking to the water's edge. I can feel the sand, first dry and then wet sand under my feet. The waves are lapping around my bare feet as the white foam of the waves crashes against the shore. The sun sparkles on the water like thousands of diamonds floating in the sea. I breathe in the salty air and I feel refreshed.

When I feel the sea air, hear the sound of the waves, feel the warmth of the sun and the coolness of the water, the beauty of this scene connects me to my own beauty, my own special qualities and virtues. Just like the sea, at times I have strength and determination and at times I am calm, still and peaceful and, just like the sea, I too have hidden depths of stillness, hidden depths of knowledge and an inner beauty that is, just by being, an expression of love. I notice how still and silent my mind has become and my thoughts are naturally drawn towards a higher beauty, the beauty of God. And once again I notice how the qualities of the sea seem to echo the qualities of this highest supreme energy source. I see how the sun shining on the water reminds me of the unlimited light of God. I feel that light and within that light I experience an eternal beauty of silent bliss, unlimited peace and power. The sparkling sea and the white foam on the waves remind me of God's beautiful fresh purity and love.

I'm aware of God as a supreme source of all that is good. I can feel a pure energy of beauty, love and peace, touching my soul. My heart opens and I absorb beauty, love and peace deep in the silence of my own inner being. Myself and God, linked by the wonder of the ocean — two free spirits in an eternal spiritual union of love. My soul feels light and refreshed, no heaviness, no burden. My deep-seated resentments are dissolving naturally and easily, as my own inner beauty emerges and as my expression of my love becomes stronger. I see how the clear water of the sea is like a reflection of the growing clarity within my soul.

In the safety of God's company I bend down and write in the sand, 'I love..., I love..', and I write the names of all the people I would like to send love to, including myself. 'I love..., I love..., I love..., I love..' And now in the safety of God's company I write, 'I forgive..., I forgive..', and then I write the names of all the people who I feel have hurt me in some way, and again I include my own name. 'I forgive..., I forgive..., I forgive..., I forgive..., I forgive..'

In my mind I see one of these people on the beach. I stabilise my feelings in the silent beauty and peace of my inner being. I'm aware that both myself and that other person are surrounded by a light of supreme divinity. I say 'I forgive you, I forgive you' and with every offer of forgiveness I make my inner spirit becomes lighter, refreshed. With forgiveness comes a deep acceptance, both of myself and of the other person, an acceptance that even within the present imperfection of each soul lie a silent beauty and love. I am at peace with that person.

Standing on the beach, I become aware of God's dream for the human race, that all human souls can fill their hearts with so much spiritual love and beauty, that they'll gain the strength to move away from mistakes of the past and move towards relationships that have respect, caring and love as their natural expression.

When I'm ready I turn from the sea and in my own time walk back, back over the warm, dry sand and I find that my thoughts are back, back in the present time and place.

(THIS COMMENTARY IS RECORDED WITH SPECIALLY COMPOSED MEDITATION MUSIC ON THE CASSETTE *MOVING ON 2.*)

Meditation Commentary – **Silent Sunrise**

I allow myself to feel calm and relaxed. With every breath in, I breathe in relaxation and with every breath out, I breathe out tension. My body is relaxing and, as I become aware of any tightness in any muscle, I let it go, relax.

And now my mind: I let go of any heaviness, tension, worries or doubts in my thoughts. They drift away and I allow calmness and peace to enter my mind.

I imagine that I am standing on a deserted beach at dawn and the silent sun is rising over the sea. The sun is glowing pink and gold behind the delicate clouds. The light of the sun is bringing beauty, harmony and silence. There's no sound, and my mind is still. The rising sun is filling me with warmth and light. I am surrounded by beauty, by harmony and peace.

And now my thoughts open up like a path inward, towards my inner self. I have courage to cross any obstacles of my inner weaknesses or doubts and begin to explore the silent spaces within myself.

I am becoming lighter. The form of my body is shimmering with light, and from the centre of my being I feel a warm glow of peace and light. Feelings of calmness and peace are emerging from deep within me. My thinking has become still and I become the essence of peace itself, calm, silent serenity, just like the silent sunrise.

As I go deeper within myself, I notice that the silent sun over the sea is rising higher in the sky. The rays from the sun are becoming stronger and warmer. I allow these rays to penetrate my inner self. I feel my heart reaching out to catch the beauty and harmony, and now the path of my thoughts is taking me beyond even the sun, onwards, outwards, yearning towards the brightest energy of creation, towards the Supreme Being of light, of love and of peace, onward to the source of all beauty and harmony, outward to God.

I feel the presence of love around me. Warm vibrations of peace and love surround me. I feel protected, cared for, free from heaviness and there is joy and contentment in my heart. I'm light, I'm free, I'm peace.

I give myself a gift of forgiveness. I am strong enough to let go of all the mistakes of the past and fears of the future. They drift away out of my consciousness like steam dissolving into space. I move away from the limitations I'd placed upon myself in the form of doubts and expectations and I allow myself to be free. I respect myself. I have faith in myself. I am OK, just to be me. I don't have to put on a mask for the world to see because, when I accept myself, others will accept me too, whoever or whatever I am.

As my own heart fills with peace, joy, acceptance of myself, I begin to share these qualities with others. I give my acceptance and forgiveness to others or whomever I choose in the form of a gift, a gift of love from my heart. As I give love and accept others, even those who I feel have hurt me, then the chains around my heart open up and I become free, free from the jail of my thoughts, free to experience myself as I truly am. I'm satisfied, content, peaceful. I let go of unfulfilled expectations and I become free of fear, free of worry and guilt.

Life is a game in which I make the rules. I choose to play the game of life with clarity in my thoughts and easiness and lightness in my attitudes. I flow with the game of life and I allow it to unfold itself. I accept the surprises and changes life is offering me with confidence and calmness. I accept the challenge of life and I resolve to live every day in freedom, with lightness in my heart and easiness in my mind.

The ever-present, divine being of light, the Supreme Being of peace and love, showers blessings on my effort in the form of rays of light and love. I feel these vibrations of light and love and I accept them within my heart.

Now it's time for my thoughts to return. As I return, I keep within myself feelings of lightness and freedom. I resolve to play the game of life with easiness and acceptance, to remain free in my thoughts and my attitudes, free just to be me.

(THIS COMMENTARY IS RECORDED WITH SPECIALLY COMPOSED MEDITATION MUSIC ON THE CASSETTE *MOVING ON 2.*)

Chapter 6 TRANSITION

Finding contentment in life and death and experiencing peace and radiance

If the experience of a life-threatening illness has come into my life, there is at least one thing of which I can be absolutely sure: that change has become necessary in my health, my roles, my lifestyle, my attitudes and the way I experience myself.

Deep inside myself, in my subconscious mind, I may have known for a long time that some change and growth have been needed in the way I am experiencing my life. Perhaps I have ignored this, been too busy to think about it or it's been too difficult to face. However, there is a close relationship between my body (including my immune system) and my deepest inner feelings and experiences. My body will reflect the tensions that I myself try to ignore. Something inside myself is stopping me from really 'living' and now my body has begun to reflect this — it has begun to die.

Through the pain and trauma of this experience, I need to re-assess my concepts of what my 'living' is all about — what it means really 'to live'. My life is a very personal thing. However, the experience of peace, contentment and happiness is perhaps the common goal of us all. If I have tried all avenues of treatment and my hopes for recovery have not been fulfiled, then I am confronted with having to come to terms with the issue of death itself.

Is it possible to face my own death and find new growth within the self, leading to peace, contentment and happiness? The answer has to be 'yes', not just because many have experienced this, but also because death is a natural and intrinsic part of life and may itself lead to new growth. For instance, many have experienced that death may be the end of the body, but this does not necessarily mean the end of the 'self'.

I first need to look at what death means to me — my own reactions, my own fears. This is useful, even if I am not facing the immediate prospect of death because, as I consider death, it is my life that will come before me — my achievements, failures, attitudes, beliefs, experiences of the self, my relationships.

For some, death is too hard to contemplate and I must respect this. Some will deny they are dying to their last breath or they will spend their last moments blaming others for their situation. This is their choice and I must allow them that. However, if I can find the courage to face my own death and, therefore, the reality of my life, I am giving myself the opportunity to grow and change and to learn how really to live.

The experience of a life-threatening illness can bring a stillness within the self whereby I can experience myself as I truly am, whereby I am able to find my own solutions, both to the unresolved issues in my life and in achieving what I really want in my life. Furthermore, when facing death, I can often discover within myself new potentials, new creativity and even a new awareness to do with God and the meaning of life.

To face death means to face fears of the unknown, fears about where I am going and fears about how I am going to get there. We are all capable of resolving these questions in our own unique and individual way. However, I must allow myself the opportunity to do so. This process is one of deep reflection and meditation along with acceptance of the self, including acceptance of all I have been and done and acceptance of what I am now.

ACCEPTANCE

Acceptance can be the final outcome of all my emotions, strivings, growth and effort to come to terms with myself and the matter of dying. Acceptance is the product of emotional, mental and spiritual healing within the self. Acceptance means complete contentment with myself, my situation, my relationships with God and with all that life has given and taken away. Contentment is the experience of living in the here and now in a peaceful and meaningful way, beyond the influence of the past, the future, others, circumstances, my own weaknesses or bodily discomfort.

Contentment and acceptance mean I can use what I have in the best possible way without bitterness and resentment about what I don't or won't have. This means I have accepted my 'whole' self, the mental, emotional, spiritual and physical aspects of the self, including the illness.

Acceptance will come from my willingness to let go: to push aside worries about trivialities and unresolved parts of myself and to face and resolve my fears, shame, guilt and other unfinished business. I will then emerge as more self-respecting, more self-loving and more courageous, able to face whatever obstacles come in my direction.

The final stage of death from a terminal illness is a slow movement of consciousness away from this world and away from the body. It can be of great help for the family to understand that this is not a rejection. At this time, when a person has achieved a stage of acceptance, the face reflects this and can look peaceful and radiant, in spite of the degeneration of the body. This is the dignity of the person who has resolved the issues of pain and discomfort, future fears, past mistakes and relationships.

If I am dying and can share my thoughts and feelings with my family members or others, then they too may be more able to share their own thoughts and feelings. Acceptance and peace in death do not mean there won't be grief and an adjustment process for those left behind. However, the pain of separation may be eased when feelings have been open, shared, accepted and worked through together.

If others experience the courage, strength and acceptance of their dying loved one, this may help them to face their own resentment, regret, sorrow and guilt. These mutual growth experiences can lead to an accepting silence in the relationship that goes beyond words. It is the experience of the gladness to have lived and the acceptance of death.

To face death with acceptance, self-respect and courage is something individuals have to decide to do on their own terms, when they are ready. It is not something they can do when they are not ready, simply to please others. If I want to help others reach the stage of acceptance in dying, then I must be ready to be there, to listen, to share and to be careful I don't project my own needs onto the dying person.

In order to do this, I must get in touch with my own feelings, fears, unfinished business and attitudes towards death. Not everyone will reach a stage of acceptance at the time of death. However, ultimately, it is my own choice whether I want to work towards a stage of peace and acceptance or not. This is true in life as well as in the process of dying.

The experience of peace and acceptance within the self will come from my own efforts to choose my own path, to change my attitudes, to experience my inner self and my deepest positive qualities, to resolve relationships and to let go of future fears and past hurts.

Meditation is a valuable tool in this process as it allows me to experience the stillness, depth and acceptance within the self, thereby giving me the courage and strength to work through these issues. Meditation begins a clearing process within the mind, which opens up realms of truth that lie locked within the self. I begin to experience the inner self and consciousness as free and independent from the body, my ill-health and my role.

I become thereby more ready and capable of perceiving and experiencing higher truths to do with God and/or the nature of life itself. The greatest resource I have is myself, wherein lie all questions, all answers, all solutions and all truth. Moreover, through meditation, I can begin to 'live' my 'truths' or beliefs and thereby give them power. For instance, I can experience death as being a transition to peace in whatever form I choose. I can begin this process firstly by using my imagination and then, as I meditate, my thoughts gradually become feelings and experiences within the self.

Meditation Commentary – **Moving On**

I focus my thoughts and with the eye of my mind I look deep within my inner self. I connect with the feelings of my own natural and positive qualities. A warm feeling of calmness and peace emerges from deep within myself and fills my consciousness with feelings of contentment and tranquillity. All other images fall away from my mind. Thoughts of my daily concerns and the activities of my body all drift away. I let them go. As I let them go, I become free.

My mind is light, lost in the feelings of my own eternal qualities. I am the form of peace, in harmony with myself and in harmony with life. I feel the light-energy that is me, generating vibrations of peace and harmony. I feel a deep acceptance of life and I observe my destiny pulling me ever onward.

I see a path of light stretching out in front of me, a pathway of light. I contemplate this pathway. I have no fear. I only feel at peace with myself. As I walk hand in hand with my destiny, my nature and my inner being feel steady. My thoughts hold these feelings of stability and confidence within myself. I'm a beam of light that gently caresses the rough edges of life and flows over and around them. I'm free to be me.

I know I have the strength and power to delve into life's deepest secrets and then to emerge with understanding and beauty, radiating peace.

Filled with feelings of lightness and freedom, I begin my journey down the pathway of light. I am not alone. With each step I feel safe, protected and guided. A supreme energy source of light from beyond the universe is sending me waves of peace and love. It's as if I am in the company of a true friend, a friend who is always there, a friend who is reliable, trustworthy and caring. I feel vibrations from the supreme energy source surrounding me with waves of peace and love and I absorb these within myself. I feel totally at peace with myself and love emerges from my heart, love and acceptance for myself and for my destiny.

My love travels outwards and touches the supreme, divine energy of God. It is a union of love, a meeting of hearts. I'm surrounded by light, immersed in the ocean of peace, the ocean of love.

I'm free from the chains of my worldly life. Waves of joy caress my own inner being of light. My pathway of light has now taken me far beyond the pull of the world, outward to merge within the supreme light of silence and peace. I am loved and accepted by this supreme being of light. This is bringing clarity within my inner being, washing away all that is old and unnecessary within me, washing away all the old and unnecessary. I begin to sparkle and shine like a jewel. I become the form of peace and joy and I radiate these qualities from the depth of my being. I am peaceful, I am content, I am free, I am me.

My eye of understanding opens and I experience the truth that lies deep within myself. I am at peace with myself and the part that I play on the stage of the world. I am unique. I am worthy to achieve whatever destination I place in front of myself.

I have the wisdom and intuitive knowledge to answer all my own questions, about myself, about God, about the meaning of life.

My own truth, peace and acceptance are lighting up inside me like an inner glow, an imperishable inner light that will never dim. Life may change, my role, my form, my body may change, but my inner light always travels steadily on to new experiences, new opportunities, new growth and new life.

I let the past go and I watch it drift away. I look ahead down the path of light to my destiny and beyond and I feel released. I can go forward. I am protected and I have no fear. I accept myself and the love of the highest source of divine energy and light is guiding me with beams of love and protection. I accept this guidance. I accept this light. I'm surrounded by joy, peace and love. I surrender, I'm free, I'm me.

I have journeyed far into the depth of my inner being. My search for the truth has led me both inward to myself and outward far beyond myself. Both merge in the totality of truth itself.

Now it's time to bring my thoughts back to the room in which I am sitting, back to my bodily form, my name. Yet, even as I sit here, truth and peace still shine through my eyes and my face. I am glowing with love and contentment. I'm still free.

(THIS COMMENTARY IS RECORDED WITH SPECIALLY COMPOSED MEDITATION MUSIC ON THE CASSETTE *MOVING ON 2.*)

Chapter 7 SPIRITUALITY: THE POWER TO CHANGE
Knowing God through stillness and meditation

I live in a society where a concern for physical well-being is often dominant. How much time is left in the day after I have catered for my physical needs – cooking, earning, cleaning, resting? Yet to do this over a long period of time is seemingly to deny the reality that I am more than a physical body. I have feelings, thoughts and emotions, all of which are an expression of my inner being.

To concentrate solely on my physical existence means that my inner spirit can feel unnurtured and empty. I may have wealth and physical comforts but a true feeling of inner peace and happiness may continue to elude me. If my inner spirit feels unnurtured, peaceless or discontented, then I may rely more on my body, external achievements and good health as a source of well-being in my life. However, if I lose my health, then my feelings of well-being also disappear.

Many people are recognising that for total health and well-being individuals must develop and balance their inner existence and spirituality with their external physical needs.

Many people at a time of sorrow or trauma in their lives turn to religion or God as a source of comfort and for the nurturing of the inner self. A small child who has fallen over and hurt itself instinctively looks to its guardian for protection and help. In a similar way the experience of a life-threatening illness can bring feelings of having lost one's way on the highway of life.

Feeling unprotected, scared and alone, I may instinctively search for my spiritual guardian, for God, in whatever form that may be for me.

However, by itself, the desire to know God is not enough. How can I really experience who and where God is? How can I communicate with this highest, most divine source? How can I really feel the love and protection of God?

Ultimately, what I am seeking is a 'true' experience of God or an experience of the reality of absolute love, divinity, wisdom and truth of God, an experience that goes beyond thinking and is felt in my heart, an experience through which I can clearly understand that God is real and He is my companion, protector, guide and even teacher and saviour.

The first step is to begin with my own concepts and beliefs about the highest most divine energy I call God. My aim is to develop and extend my own beliefs and concepts and experience the reality of them.

Through meditation I learn to take my thoughts beyond the physical body, upward and outward to a dimension of infinite peace and stillness, a place where I can find supreme energy and light, a region of silence, a place where I can find the supreme being who resonates with the pure infinite and eternal qualities of love, peace, bliss, purity and benevolent acceptance.

As I meditate I begin to focus and fix my thoughts on this supreme, divine being of light and, as I do this, there will come a moment when I begin to experience the qualities of God. The process is similar to when we communicate with each other and we experience each other's vibrations, moods and feelings. However, God is a bodiless being and I need to develop the subtlety in my thinking to pick up the vibrations of God without the signals of the body.

Meditation is a process of taking one's thoughts away from mundane matters of physical existence and exploring the depths of one's own inner spiritual being and ultimately finding one's essence of silence and peace.

In the stillness of my inner being, I develop an awareness and acceptance of myself, of who I am and my connection to the events of life around me. As I do this, I develop the power to experience and know who God is. I begin to feel the vibration of God. For instance, I may have the experience of being totally loved: vibrations of love reaching out to me, surrounding me, immersing me in feelings of love, acceptance and protection. This is a love that is unconditional, a love that doesn't demand, expect or desire but simply accepts me, no matter what I've done, a love that focuses only on my strength and thereby begins to help me have a positive view of myself.

Through meditation I can experience other divine qualities of God, such as peace, bliss, serenity. I may experience each of the qualities of God individually or, ultimately, all together. As I feel and absorb these divine qualities, similar qualities emerge in myself. As I deeply experience my own positive and divine qualities, my inner being or spirit automatically starts to heal.

The most essential food for the spirit is love. A real experience of the divine energy and love of God will re-ignite the light of my inner being and begin to heal the hurts and traumas I have experienced or am experiencing.

I have often looked for such a love in human beings and have perhaps been let down. Now I can experience that, as I fill myself with the spiritual love of God, I naturally become more loving to others and less demanding that they give me love, support and recognition. When my support is from a spiritual source, I become independent and self-nurturing. I learn how to sustain myself mentally, emotionally and spiritually.

Picking up the elevated divine vibrations of God is a bit like tuning a radio to reach the right station. I have to set my consciousness and thinking in the right way. I have to remove questions of why, what, how, when, where from my mind, as well as thoughts of doubt and inadequacy or fear and confusion. This begins to allow me to experience myself as I truly am, that is, as an inner spiritual being of light which, in its purest, original state, is full of positivity, joy, peace, love and acceptance, regardless of the condition of the physical body. In this way I free myself from trivial, mundane matters and allow my own inner truth to emerge.

The truth of God, myself and even the drama of life is as close as my fingertips — I just need to learn to seek it in the right way. Every human soul has the right to know truth. Yet I need to understand that I must search for and find truth in the depth of my own silence. I don't need to argue, debate or question another person's truth or even to prove my own. When I find my own truth within myself, it is enough that this truth sits quietly within and that I develop the strength calmly to accept others who may be following different paths in life, spiritual or otherwise.

I also need to realise that I don't have to ask for help from God or others, but I need to recognise the help that is being offered to me and every human soul and to take this help as a right. After all, why do most people remember God in some form or another, particularly in times of sorrow? It is because I remember that Supreme Being as a source of light and might. Such a source has the power to renew what is old, to transform negative energy into positive, to make the inner spirit whole again, to reverse the destruction of spirituality within the self and to allow me to know and spiritually heal myself, regardless of the condition of the physical body.

Simply to experience love and peace, both within myself and from God, is not enough. Ultimately, as I increase my spiritual awareness, I come to realise the important link between my actions and my inner experience of life. God doesn't respond to my success or otherwise in achieving fame or recognition in life. The Supreme Being responds to my sincere attempts to live in this world with understanding and in harmony with myself, others and the world in general, that is, a sincere desire to create good in my own mind and give good to others. Increasing my own internal strength gives me the power to develop attitudes and perform actions that are harmonious and giving, even if I myself am the target of negative moods, words or actions of others.

As I create good attitudes and am harmonious in my actions, I develop a pride in myself that is not ego, and my self-respect increases. However, I reap the benefit of my good thoughts and actions in another way as well because, for any act of giving to others, we earn the return of that good act in some way at some time. 'As we sow, so shall we reap.' If I repeatedly treat others with sincere good wishes and respect, even if they are not returning good wishes and respect to me, eventually they will start changing the way they are interacting with me. They will respond because, ultimately, all human beings respond to sincerity, respect and love. The process may take a long time but, through it, I can develop a lot of strength, learning, power and wisdom. I need to pay attention to my own actions and to understand the actions of others — they are often trapped in the chains of their own weaknesses and I won't help them by being affected by their negativity.

Truly spiritual beings are those who treat their fellow human beings with equality, sincerity, gentleness, tact, respect and love. This is spirituality in action which strengthens my own internal spiritual development. A person who is the embodiment of such qualities is coming closer to the nature of God and so naturally develops a close relationship with God.

The response of God comes through vibrations but, also, this spiritual relationship gives me the power of realisation through which I can become an observer of my own part and of the world stage. I thereby develop an understanding of how I myself need to take responsibility for such a change.

The development of my spiritual self and my relationship with God will not necessarily lead to miraculous cures of the physical body. However, it will lead to the healing of my inner spirit.

Healing the imbalances and negativity of my inner spirit often addresses the original or the initial source of the present physical illness.

Healing the inner self brings joy, peace and love back to my life experience, regardless of the state of my health, finances and external roles. I am in control of the way I experience my reality, regardless of what the drama of life brings my way. I have exercised my choice to live.

Meditation Commentary – **The Power to Change**

I allow my original qualities of easiness and peace to enter my consciousness. I choose to remove all doubts, questions and other thoughts from my mind. I have a right to experience peace and serenity in my life. I don't have to ask for peace or search for peace. This quality already belongs to me.

From deep within myself I emerge the feeling of peace. I experience peaceful vibrations, rising up from within myself and gently caressing my mind, surrounding my inner self with silence and tranquillity. Now I can relax and take a rest from the constant racing of my own thoughts and allow myself to experience who I truly am, a being of peace, a being of light, a being of silence. I am peaceful and light. I'm beyond the pull of circumstances or the nature of others. Now even my body sets me free and I can travel upwards, outwards to a dimension of silence and peace, my original home, a home of rest, a home of infinite light, a home of unending peace.

I become aware of a point-energy of light, like a star, radiating infinite light, sending the vibrations of light and love which touch the very depths of myself. This supreme energy of light and love is sending me a vision of myself. I am free. I'm worthy to be loved. I have the clarity and depth within my intellect to experience my destiny as I choose. I am the creator of my own reality. I have the strength to glide across the troubled waters of life, safe in the boat of my own determination and positive attitudes. I'm not alone. My heart accepts the love and guidance from my infinite, divine star of light, the light of God. I am loved, just as I am, no demands, no expectations, just the pure love of total acceptance. I become full of love and gladness. The broken pieces of my heart become filled with the warmth, love and self-respect that radiate to me from my divine star of light, and the broken pieces join together, making me whole again.

I accept this infinite light of love and I merge into an ocean of limitless love and peace. I sit with God as a Father and I feel my Father's protection and guidance. I rest with God as a Mother and I feel my Mother, loving and nurturing me. I enjoy the company and acceptance of God as my Friend. I experience true love from God, my Beloved. I experience the lightness and joy of the child in the nature of God.

My relationships with God, the supreme, infinite star of light, love and peace, have become a reality. I can let go of abstract images of the past and in a most simple way, catch the vibration, energy and power of God with my mind, the vibrations of infinite peace and love, the energy that gives me power to realise my own strengths and true purpose of my life and the power to make my deepest wishes and dreams a reality. Lightness and joy dance within me. I'm filled with strength and optimism. I have found the path to truth. I am true. All becomes silent and clear, suspended in the love of God and a deep respect for myself.

I'm free. The chains of life and of my own mind no longer bind me. I can experience life in a natural way, free from sorrow and stable in happiness.

Now it's time to bring my thoughts back to the room in which I'm sitting. I hold within *my heart the experience of the silent, peaceful land beyond, where resides the brightest star of creation, an infinite light of peace and love, the light of God. I maintain within myself feelings of lightness, joy, clarity, truth and self-respect, my own original qualities, my own true nature of peace. All I have to do is just be and all I have to be is what I am, a peaceful being of light and of love.*

(THIS COMMENTARY IS RECORDED WITH SPECIALLY COMPOSED MEDITATION MUSIC ON THE CASSETTE *MOVING ON 2*.)

Resource Information

The commentaries in *Moving On* have been recorded on the cassettes *Moving On 1* and *Moving On 2*. For easy reference, a list follows which indicates where each commentary appears, both in the text and on the cassettes.

Title	Page Numbers	Cassette Location
Orbs of Light	11,12,13	*Moving On 1*, side A
The Forest	14,15	*Moving On 1*, side A
Balloon	23, 24, 25	*Moving On 1*, side A
Inner Self	25, 26, 27	*Moving On 1*, side B
Self-esteem	34, 35	*Moving On 1*, side B
Acceptance	43, 44, 45	*Moving On 1*, side B
Forgiveness	52, 53, 54	*Moving On 2*, side A
Silent Sunrise	54, 55, 56	*Moving On 2*, side A
Moving On	63, 64, 65	*Moving On 2*, side B
The Power to Change	73, 74, 75	*Moving On 2*, side B

The following meditation cassettes will be of additional benefit:

Creative Meditation 1
Creative Meditation 2
Link of Life
Soul Journey
The Radiant Soul
Time Out

Many books and cassettes on positive thinking and meditation are published by ETERNITY INK, the publisher for the Brahma Kumaris World Spiritual University.

For enquiries contact:
ETERNITY INK, 78 Alt Street, Ashfield NSW 2131 Australia,
Tel (02) 9716 7066, Fax (02) 9799 3490.
www.bkwsuau.com.au

If you wish to find out about meditation courses offered by the Brahma Kumaris World Spiritual University, contact the main centre closest to you:

AUSTRALIA, 78 Alt St Ashfield NSW 2131, Tel (02) 9716 7066
BRAZIL, R. Dr Estevam de Almeida, 53/69, Sao Paulo, SP 05014-010, Tel (11) 864 3694
HONG KONG, 17 Dragon Rd Causeway Bay, Tel (5) 2806 3008
INDIA, 25 New Rohtak Rd Karol Bagh, New Delhi, 110005, Tel (11) 362 6961
KENYA, PO Box 12349, Maua Close, off Parklands Rd Westlands, Nairobi, Tel (2) 743 572
UK, 65 Pound Lane, London NW10 2HH, UK, Tel (20) 8727 3350
USA, Global Harmony House, 46 South Middle Neck Rd NY 11021, Tel (516) 773 0971

or www.bkwsu.com

About the Author

Margaret Pinkerton is a social worker, counselling youth and their families at Sylvania Community Health Centre, Sydney. She has two children. Margaret has been a student and teacher of Raja Yoga meditation for more than eight years. She teaches a meditation program in the Cancer Care Centre at St George Hospital, Kogarah. *Moving On* has been written from both her personal life experiences as well as the knowledge she has gained through the practice of Raja Yoga meditation. The meditation commentaries included in *Moving On: Pathways to personal growth* have been recorded to accompany the content of this book.

Acknowledgements

The meditation *Orbs of Light* is based on an Erevna meditation and is reprinted here with kind permission of Kyriacos C. Markides, Professor of Sociology, University of Maine and author of *The Magus of Strovolos: the extraordinary world of a spiritual healer*. Penguin (Arkana), London, 1990.